Nonsense Rhymes Collection

Nonsense Rhymes Collection

Nonsense Nursery Rhymes

Poems by Richard Edwards   *Illustrated by* Chris Fisher

Nonsense Counting Rhymes

Poems by Kaye Umansky   *Illustrated by* Chris Fisher

Nonsense Animal Rhymes

Poems by Kaye Umansky   *Illustrated by* Chris Fisher

OXFORD
UNIVERSITY PRESS

For Alice, David and Helen.

Love C.F.

Nonsense Nursery Rhymes

A a

Andy Dandy's legs were bandy,
Andy's legs were bent,
Through Andy Dandy's bandy legs
The trains to Scotland went.

Bb

Bobby Shafto's gone to sea,
Sailing with a chimpanzee,
They'll be back at half past three,
Bonnie Bobby Shafto.

C c

Cock a doodle doo!
I think I've caught the flu,
Shiver, shiver, cough, cough,
Atchoo! Atchoo! Atchoo!

Dd

Doctor Foster went to Gloucester
On a winter's day.
An icicle froze
On the end of his nose
And didn't fall off till May.

E e

Elsie Marley looks so fine,
Dancing down the washing line.
Will you be my valentine,
Lovely Elsie Marley?

Ff

Fee fi fo fum
Little Freddie's looking glum.
How to make him giggle?
Give his toe a wiggle.

G g

Georgie Porgie, pudding and pie,
Thought he'd catch a fish to fry,
Cast a line above his head,
Caught an aeroplane instead.

H h

Humpty Dumpty sat on a wall,
Humpty Dumpty had a great fall.
He didn't get bruised, he didn't get bumped,
Humpty Dumpty bungee-jumped.

Ii

I had a little nut tree,
I gave the tree a whack,
The tree said "Oi!
You naughty boy!"
And whacked me sharply back.

J j

Jack Sprat could eat no fat,
No sausages, no stew,
His beard was much too bristly
And it wouldn't let things through.

Kk

Katie Beardie had a cow
That learnt to drive. Don't ask me how.
The other cows just moo or sleep,
But Katie's cow goes Beep! Beep! Beep!

L l

Little Bo Peep has washed her sheep,

They'd got so grey and greasy,

But after a scrub

In a soapy tub

They came out white and fleecy.

M m

Mary, Mary, quite contrary,
What does your garden hide?
Beetles and bugs,
Slithery slugs
And shells with snails inside.

Nn

N ellie Bligh
Caught a fly
And kept it as a pet,
Taking it to school with her
To learn the alphabet.

Oo

Old King Cole was a merry old soul,
His crown was tall and twisty.
It had a flashing light on top
For when the nights were misty.

P p

Pussy cat, pussy cat, where have you been?
Under the waves in a submarine,
Pussy cat, pussy cat, what did you see?
A wobbly jellyfish goggling at me.

Q q

The Queen of Hearts she made some tarts,

From spiders, dust and soil

And broken bricks

And stones and sticks

And squirts of engine oil.

Rr

Rain, rain, go away,
You're shrinking me, I fear,
Please won't you stop?
Another drop
Will make me disappear.

S s

Simple Simon bought a pie,
But when he took a bite
A caterpillar wriggled out
To spoil his appetite.

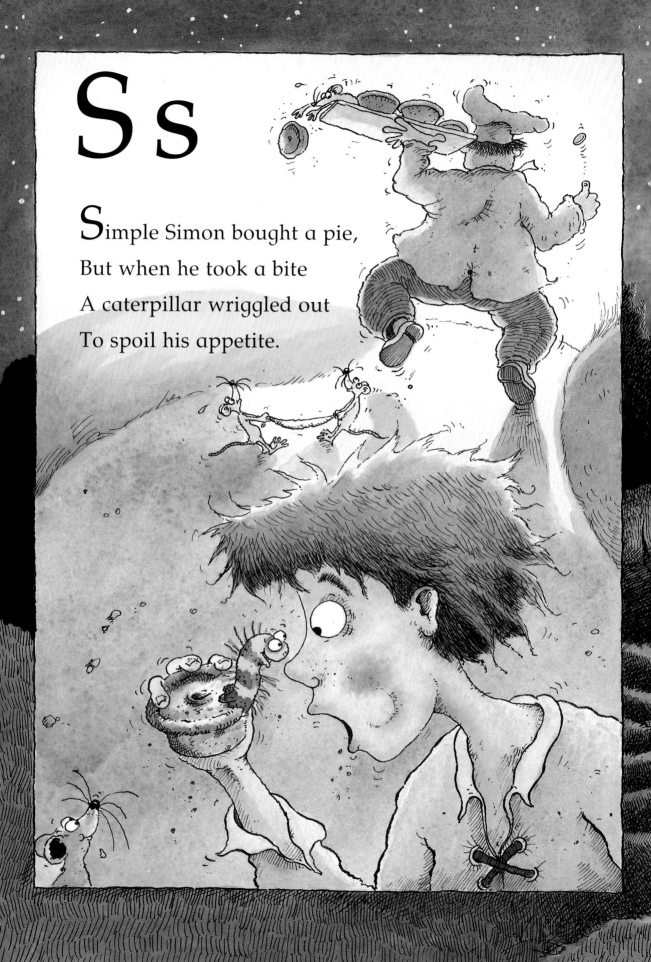

Tt

Twinkle, twinkle, little frog,
Shivering in your puddle,
Hop out of the soggy bog —
Come and have a cuddle.

U u

Up and down the city road,
Round and round the market,
Riding on my dinosaur,
Wherever can I park it?

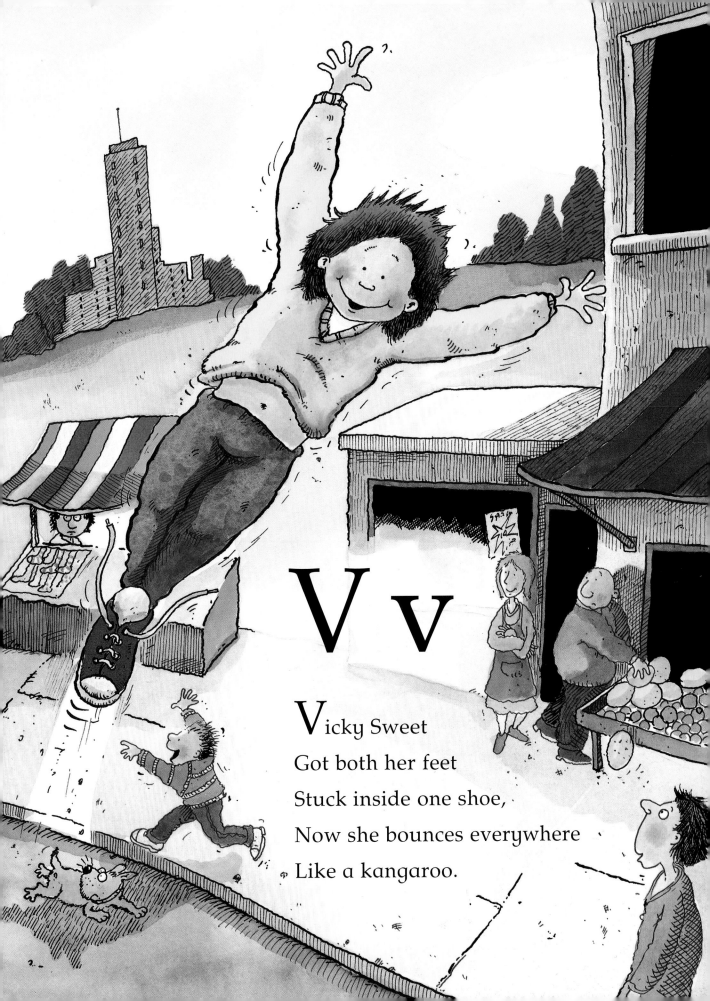

V v

Vicky Sweet
Got both her feet
Stuck inside one shoe,
Now she bounces everywhere
Like a kangaroo.

W w

Wee Willie Winkie runs through the street,
Shoes on his hands, gloves on his feet,
People are pointing all over town,
Wee Willie Winkie's upside down.

Xx

X was an eXplorer,
He explored the mountain heights
In an orange balaclava
And a pair of purple tights.

Yy

Yankee Doodle came to town,
Did he take the bus?
No, he put a saddle
On a hippopotamus.

Z z

Zackary Dapp
Started to flap,
Started to flutter and squawk,
Climbed on a chair,
Jumped in the air
And flew round the room like a hawk.

Traditional Nursery Rhymes

Do you know any nursery rhymes that begin with A, V, X, or Z? No?
Well neither do we!

B

Bobby Shafto's gone to sea,
Silver buckles at his knee;
He'll come back and marry me,
Bonny Bobby Shafto!

C

Cock a doodle doo!
My dame has lost her shoe,
My master's lost his fiddlestick,
And knows not what to do.

D

Doctor Foster went to Gloucester
In a shower of rain;
He stepped in a puddle,
Right up to his middle,
And never went there again.

E

Elsie Marley is grown so fine,
She won't get up to feed the swine,
But lies in bed till eight or nine.
Lazy Elsie Marley.

F

Fee fi fo fum
I smell the blood of an Englishman.

G

Georgie Porgie, pudding and pie,
Kissed the girls and made them cry;
When the boys came out to play,
Georgie Porgie ran away.

H

Humpty Dumpty sat on a wall,
Humpty Dumpty had a great fall.
All the king's horses,
And all the king's men,
Couldn't put Humpty together again.

I

I had a little nut tree,
Nothing would it bear
But a silver nutmeg
And a golden pear.

J

Jack Sprat could eat no fat,
His wife could eat no lean,
And so between them both, you see,
They licked the platter clean.

K

Katie Beardie had a coo,
Black and white about the mou';
Wasna that a dentie coo?
Dance Katie Beardie!

L

Little Bo-Peep has lost her sheep,
And doesn't know where to find them;
Leave them alone, and they'll come home,
Bringing their tails behind them.

M

Mary, Mary, quite contrary,
How does your garden grow?
With silver bells and cockle shells,
And pretty maids all in a row.

N

Nellie Bligh
Caught a fly,
Tied it to a string;
String broke
Cut its throat,
Poor little thing.

O

Old King Cole
Was a merry old soul,
And a merry old soul was he;
He called for his pipe,
And he called for his bowl,
And he called for his fiddlers three.

P

Pussy cat, pussy cat, where have you
  been?
I've been to London to look at the
  queen.
Pussy cat, pussy cat, what did you
  there?
I frightened a little mouse under her
  chair.

Q

The Queen of Hearts
She made some tarts,
All on a summer's day;
The Knave of Hearts
He stole the tarts,
And took them clean away.

R

Rain, rain, go away,
Come again another day.

S

Simple Simon met a pieman,
Going to the fair;
Says Simple Simon to the pieman,
Let me taste your ware.

T

Twinkle, twinkle, little star,
How I wonder what you are!
Up above the world so high,
Like a diamond in the sky.

U

Up and down the City Road,
In and out the Eagle,
That's the way the money goes,
Pop goes the weasel!

W

Wee Willie Winkie runs through the
  town,
Upstairs and downstairs in his night
  gown,
Rapping at the window, crying through
  the lock,
Are the children all in bed, for now it's
  eight o'clock?

Y

Yankee Doodle came to town,
Riding on a pony;
He stuck a feather in his cap
And called it macaroni.

To Cuzack - C.F.
To Zack and Luke - K.U.

Nonsense
Counting
Rhymes

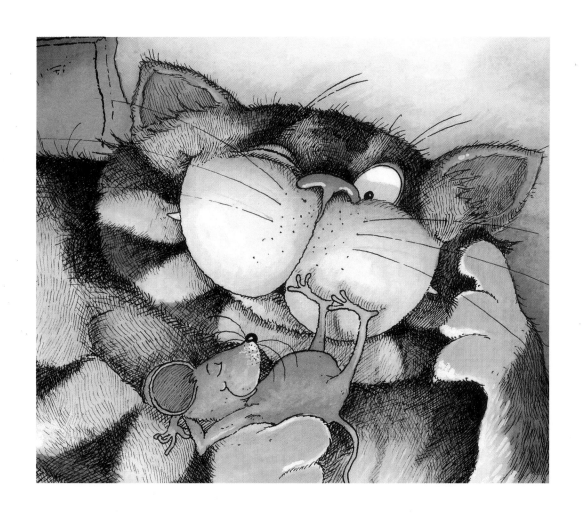

O
Zero for Nero

Emperor Nero went fishing,
"I'm sure to get hundreds," said he.
But Emperor Nero caught zero,
And had to have pizza for tea.

1
One Man Went to Mow

One man went to mow,
He couldn't work the mower,
He used a pair of scissors, so
The grass got cut much slower.

2
Two Little Dicky Birds

Two little dicky birds
Playing in the trough.
Two little sticky birds
Got a telling off.
Go and clean your feathers!
Go and wash your wings!
Don't play in the trough again,
You mucky little things!

3
Three Silly Goblins

Three silly goblins were painting a rose.

The first goblin painted the second one's nose.

The third one poured paint in the first goblin's shoe.

Were they good at the job? I don't think so, do you?

4
Four Crazy Rabbits

Over my tail and whoops a daisy!

Four rabbits going crazy.

Here comes Farmer John.

Four rabbits going...going...gone!

5
One, Two, Three, Four, Five

One, two, three, four, five,

Once I caught a shark alive,

Six, seven, eight, nine, ten,

Don't think I'll do that again!

6
Sing a Song of Sixpence

Sing a song of sixpence,

A pocket full of cheese,

Four and twenty monkeys

Swinging in the trees.

They picked all the bananas

And dropped them on my head.

I had to call the monkey king

Who sent them off to bed.

7
Seven Pirates

Shiver me timbers, set the sails,
Be sure to catch the breeze!
Seven pirates went a-sailing
On the seven salty seas.
The life was tough, the seas were rough,
They lasted seven years,
Then sailed home to their seven wives
Who gave them seven big cheers!

8
Eight Cakes

Two, four, six, eight!

Count the cakes the giant ate.

Stop him quick! He'll eat the plate!

Oh dear. Too late.

9
Nine Plump Pigeons

Three, six, nine! The day was fine.

Nine plump pigeons

Perching on the line.

The cat crept up, her jaws went snap!

And nine plump pigeons went

Flap, flap, flap!

10
Ten Tubby Teddies

Ten tubby teddies on a trampoline,
Jump, teddy, jump! Jump, teddy, jump!
Their coats are red, their hats are green,
Jump, teddy, jump! Jump, teddy, jump!
They jumped so high, they were so keen,
Jump, teddy, jump! Jump, teddy, jump!
They made a hole in the trampoline,
Thump, teddy,

thump,

thump,

THUMP!

If You Can't Sleep

"If you can't sleep, try counting sheep,
And soon you will be snoring."
That's what my mummy said to me,
But counting sheep was boring.
So I tried counting lions,
But the lions started *ROARING!*
I'm going back to sheep again.
Who said sheep were boring?

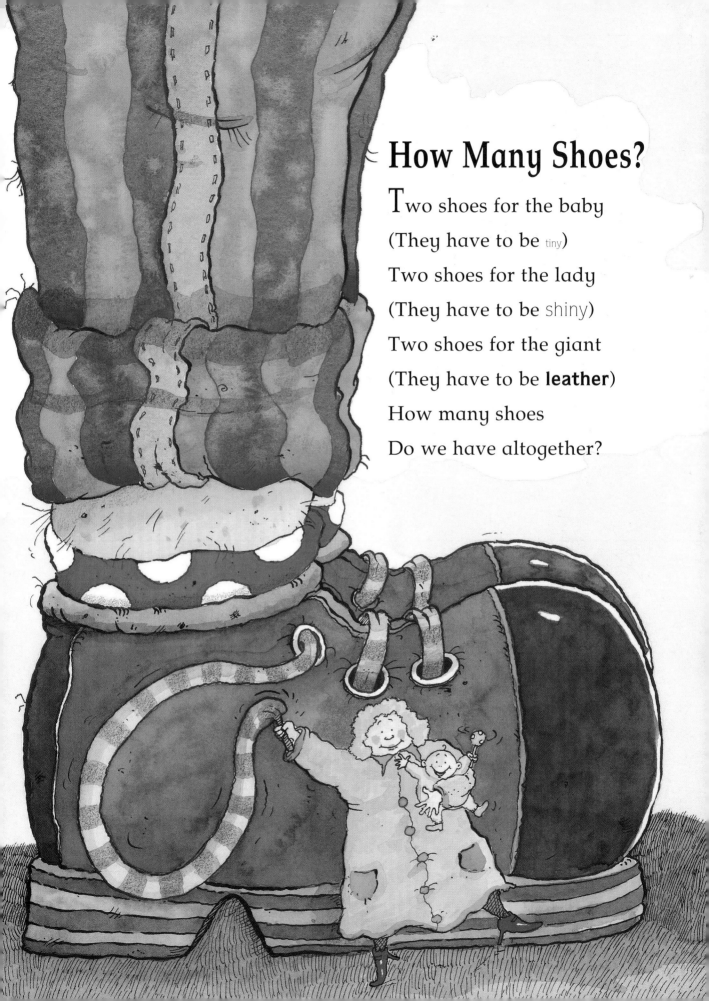

How Many Shoes?

Two shoes for the baby
(They have to be tiny)
Two shoes for the lady
(They have to be shiny)
Two shoes for the giant
(They have to be **leather**)
How many shoes
Do we have altogether?

Cockatoo Counting

One cockatoo meets one cockatoo.

Pleased to meet you. How d'you do?

Down fly another pair, that's two more.

Two cockatoos plus two make four.

When Octopuses Cuddle

When octopuses cuddle
They get into a huddle,
Counting all those tentacles
Can get you in a muddle.

Supper Time

This little pig laid the table,

This little pig stirred the pot,

This little pig laid the fire,

This little pig made it hot.

This little pig cried "Wee wee! Stew for tea!"

And ate the lot!

I Wish I was a Centipede

I wish I was a centipede.
I'd *wriggle* under roots,
And spend each evening polishing
My hundred muddy boots.
I'd build myself a little home
Beneath the mossy rocks
And spend each morning washing out
My hundred smelly socks.

There was an Old Woman

There was an old woman who lived in a welly.

The boot was Size One. Much too small, and quite smelly.

She saved up her money and moved to a shoe.

The shoe was much cleaner and bigger (Size Two).

In time, she retired to a sandal (Size Three).

It was airy and light, with a view of the sea.

She's living there still, in the warm summer sun,

And never went back to the welly (Size One).

Weigh Too Heavy

Elephants are really big
And so are killer whales.
If you tried to weigh them,
You'd surely break the scales.

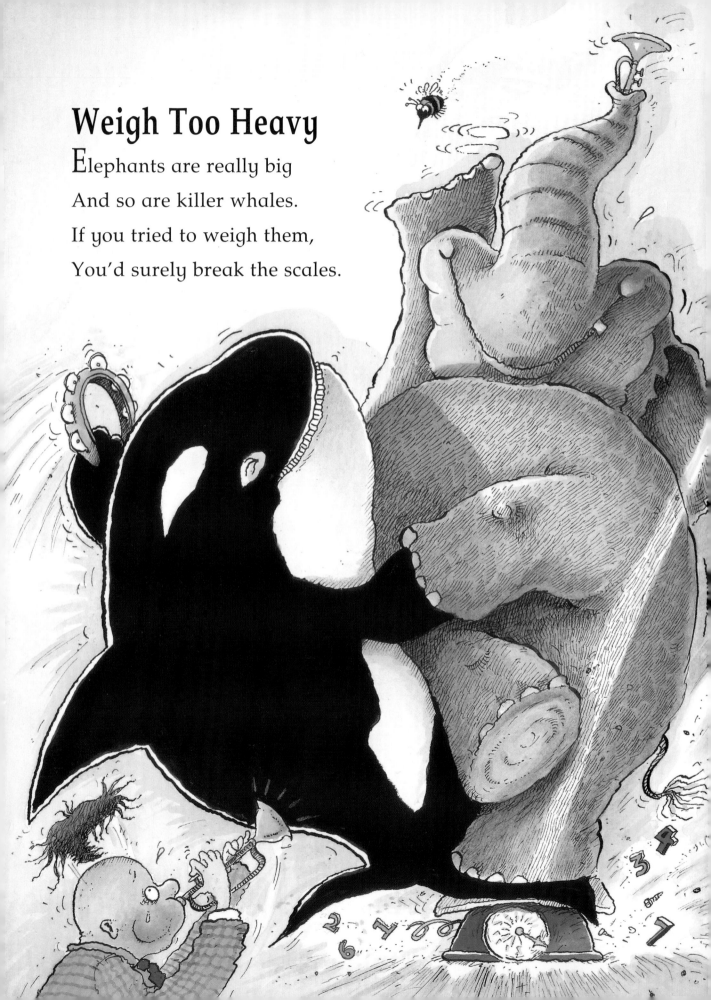

Ghostly Counting

One, two, I can go *BOO!*

Three, four, walk through the door,

Five, six, play *scaaary* tricks,

Seven, eight, haunting is great,

Nine, ten, let's do it again!

BOOooo!

Miss One, Two and Three

Miss One, Two and Three
Could never agree
On what kind of buns
They should have for their tea.
Miss One preferred currants,
Miss Two preferred plain,
Miss Three ate the lot
And was sick on the train.

The Clock Struck One

The clock struck one. The mouse ran down.

Whatever did he do?

He took an hour to climb back up,

And then the clock struck two!

All day the mouse ran up and down.

He thought, enough of that!

He lasted until midnight

Then he moved in with the cat.

Five Little Snowmen

Five little snowmen
Fishing in the loch,
One caught a cart wheel,
One caught a clock,
One caught a casket
Filled with gold.
One caught a coffee pot
And one caught a cold!

How Doth the Little Alligator

How doth the little alligator

Take away and add?

He's bought himself a calculator.

Clever little lad!

The Bears' Phone Call

345 6789?

Goldilocks is on the line!

She's ringing us from Norwich!

She says she's out of porridge!

Out of porridge? Is it true?

Whatever will the poor girl do?

We'll have to send some in the post.

'Til then, she must make do with toast.

To Mark - C.F.
To Zack and Luke - K.U.

Nonsense
Animal
Rhymes

Goldfish

Goldfish are **slippery**,

Goldfish are *wriggly*

Some are quite serious,

Some are quite *giggly*,

Some swim in circles

And wave when they pass,

Others make faces

And glare through the glass.

Wriggly, *giggly*,

Most of all, wet,

You can't beat a goldfish

If you want a pet.

Milkshakes

By day, the peaceful cows chew cud
And flick their tails in leafy shade.
At night, they turn cartwheels in mud
And that is how milkshakes are made.
My grandad says that this is true.
I think he's telling fibs, don't you?

Piggy Got Stuck Up The Chimney

Piggy got stuck up the chimney,
Piggy was much too stout,
We tied a sheet to his dangling feet,
POP! We pulled him out.

We washed him in the sunshine,
We dried him in the rain,
Then piggy got stuck up the chimney
And we had to start again.

Chess

I play chess with my cheetah.

My cheetah's name is Jim.

He has been known to beat me.

But, mostly, I beat him.

Yesterday I was defeated.

That's because my cheetah cheated.

Tortoise

I am a little tortoise,
My house is on my back.
I often stop and pop inside
To have a little snack.

And then I pop back out again
And smell the lovely flowers.
That is my daily exercise.
It takes me hours and hours.

My house is warm and cosy
And clean as a new pin.
And when my friends come calling,
I'm always out or in.

Little Birdie

Little birdie on the branch,
Very small and shy.
Tell me, birdie, can you talk?
No, kid. Can you fly?

Gorilla!

I'm a Gorilla!
I'm a Gorilla!
I want ice cream
And I want vanilla!
Three big scoops
On a dish, with a spoon.
I want ice cream
And I want it **SOON**.

Pussy Cat, Pussy Cat

Pussy cat, pussy cat,
Where have you been?
I've been sewing up socks
On the sewing machine.

Pussy cat, pussy cat,
Where are you going?
I'm off to a disco.
I'm fed up with sewing.

Lucky Ducky

Lucky Ducky
Played in muck,
Lucky Ducky
Got quite stuck.
He made the bank
Before he sank,
Plucky
    Mucky

        Yucky

        Lucky

            Ducky.

The Lazy Rooster

Here is a lazy rooster.

He will not leave his bed.

He waits for someone else to crow

And then he nods his head.

He always likes a lie in.

He is a morning hater.

They've given him a nickname –

Cock-A-Do-It-Later!

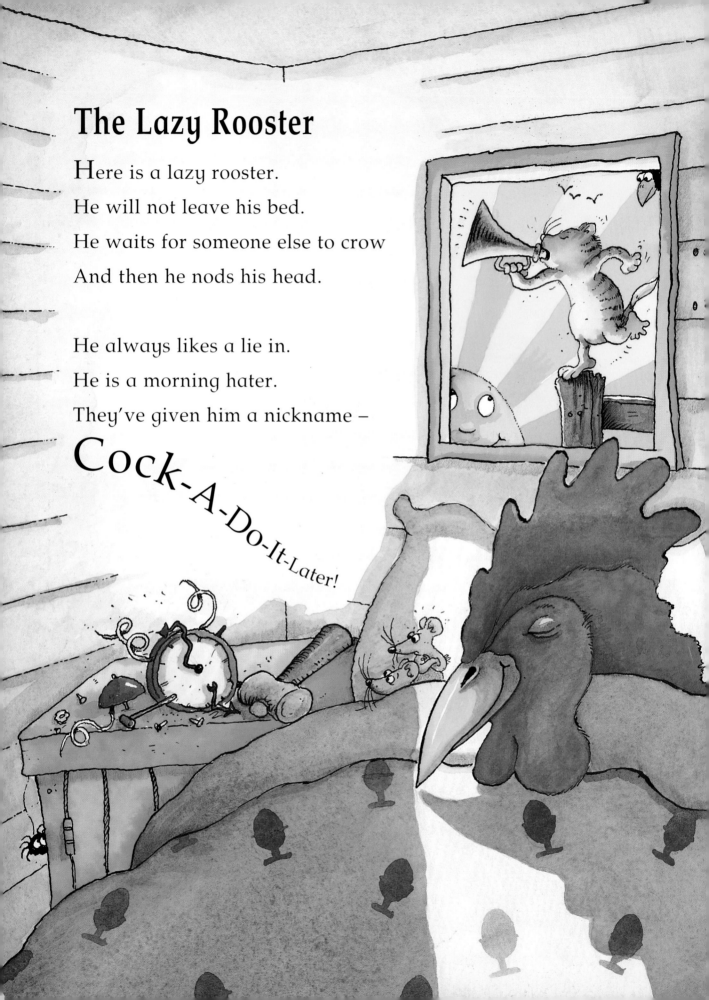

Tiger Joe

A worried young tiger called Joe
Had spots from his head to his toe.
He shouted, "Oh, cripes!
I'm supposed to have stripes!
I think I'm a leopard, you know!"

Mad Weather We're Having

It's raining cats and dogs again,
It said so on the news.
Last Sunday it rained penguins.
On Monday, kangaroos.

On Tuesday, it was froggy,
On Wednesday, cold as mice,
On Thursday, it snowed polar bears
(Which wasn't very nice.)

Friday was a fowl day,
Saturday was bats,
And now we're back to Sunday
With a load more dogs and cats.

I'd like to stay here talking
But I'm soaked right to the skin.
Now it's blowing up a buffalo!
I think I'm going in.

Elephants

Elephants are bashful,
As bashful as can be.
They always keep their trunks on
When swimming in the sea.

How unlike the polar bears,
Who do not seem to mind
And swim in freezing waters
With a polar bare behind.

Bad Hare

Harry Hare was late for school,

He dawdled in the lane.

He broke his brand new pencil

And his sums were wrong again.

He got sent off at football

And his homework blew away.

The teacher wrote his mum a note.

It was a Bad Hare Day.

St Jungles

The school is St Jungles,
And here are the staff.
Mr Gorilla
And Mrs Giraffe.
Old Mr Elephant,
Miss Chimpanzee
And Mr McMonkey
Who teaches P.E.
Ms Tiger cooks dinner,
She's one of the mums.
And Mr Puff-Adder,
He teaches us sums.

Bored

Brian the lion,
Samantha the panther
And Rita the cheetah
Were horribly bored.
So they stood on a hill
In deepest Brazil
And they roared and they roared
And they roared and they ROARED!

"Enough of this roaring,"
Said Brian the lion,
"My throat's really sore
And it's hurting my head.
I want to be quiet.
I think we should try it."
And so they went home
And played Twister™ instead.

The Wolf's Tale

I'm a Big, Bad Wolf.

My name is Keith.

I'll tell you my adventures.

I huffed and I puffed 'til I blew out my teeth

And had to get new dentures.

So now I cannot huff and puff

And am no longer snappy.

I moved in with the Little Pigs.

We're really, really happy.

Snakess and Ladderss

Calling all cobrass
And viperss and adderss!
Today is the day
We will play ssnakess and ladderss!
We'll flicker our tonguess
As we sswing from the rungss
And hisssss at the world
At the top of our lungss!

ssssSSSSSSSSSSSSS!

Poor Noah!

It's raining, it's pouring,
The lions are roaring,
The hippos are kicking
Great holes in the flooring!

The monkeys are shrieking,
The tigers aren't speaking
And both the giraffes
Are complaining of leaking.

The rabbits are jumpy,
The bears are quite grumpy,
And both of the camels
Have gone really humpy.

No wonder poor Noah
Was heard to remark
"It's hard keeping order
Inside of this ark!"

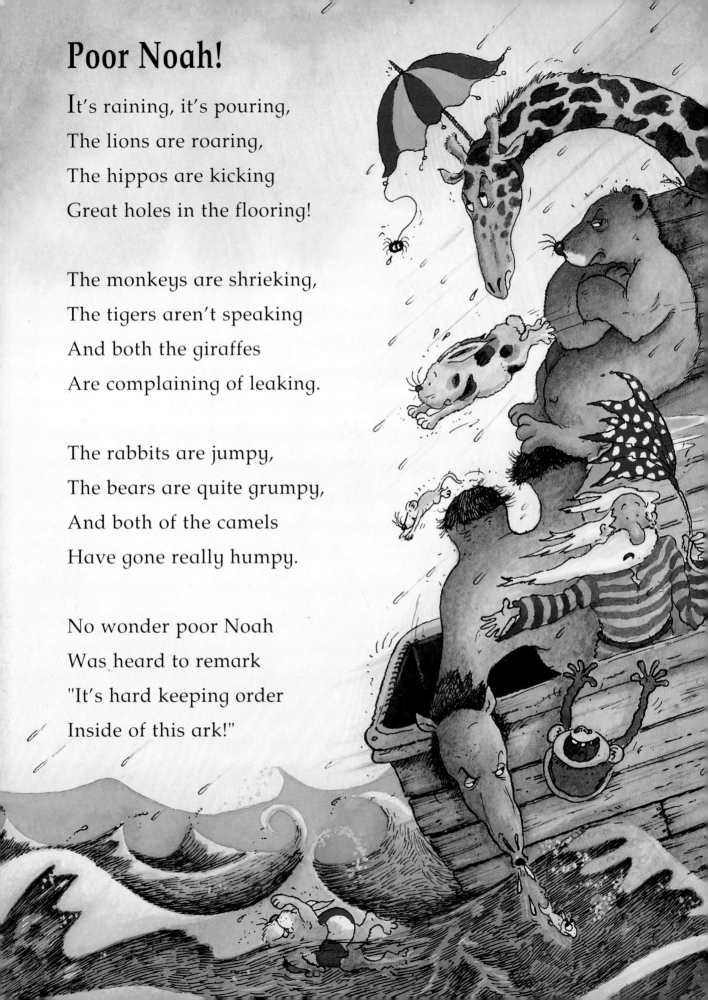

The Insect Race

Ready, steady, off they go!
The beetle's in the lead!
The grasshoppers are gaining,
With a sudden burst of speed.

The worm has turned the corner,
And the crowd begins to clap,
But the spider and the ladybird
Are closing up the gap!

They're heading for the winning post,
The pace is really fast.
The race is done. The beetle won.
And all the snails came last.

Rockaby, Crocodile

Rockaby, crocodile,

Deep in the ooze,

The moon's in the sky

And it's time for a snooze.

Tomorrow, we'll fish

In the rivers and streams.

But now it's your bedtime.

Goodnight, and sweet dreams.

OXFORD
UNIVERSITY PRESS

Great Clarendon Street, Oxford OX2 6DP

Oxford University Press is a department of the University of Oxford.
It furthers the University's objective of excellence in research, scholarship,
and education by publishing worldwide in

Oxford New York

Auckland Cape Town Dar es Salaam Hong Kong Karachi
Kuala Lumpur Madrid Melbourne Mexico City Nairobi
New Delhi Shanghai Taipei Toronto

With offices in

Argentina Austria Brazil Chile Czech Republic France Greece
Guatemala Hungary Italy Japan Poland Portugal Singapore
South Korea Switzerland Thailand Turkey Ukraine Vietnam

Oxford is a registered trade mark of Oxford University Press
in the UK and in certain other countries

British Library Cataloguing in Publication Data

Data available

ISBN-13: 978-0-19-911479-5
ISBN-10: 0-19-911479-X

1 3 5 7 9 10 8 6 4 2

Printed in China by Imago